Pet Shop Boys
The Hits

HAL•LEONARD®

Published by

Hal Leonard

Exclusive distributors:

Hal Leonard
7777 West Bluemound Road
Milwaukee, WI 53213
Email: info@halleonard.com

Hal Leonard Europe Limited
42 Wigmore Street
Marylebone, London, W1U 2RN
Email: info@halleonardeurope.com

Hal Leonard Australia Pty. Ltd.
4 Lentara Court
Cheltenham, Victoria, 3192 Australia
Email: info@halleonard.com.au

Order No. AM89450
ISBN 0-7119-3032-5
This book © Copyright 2004 by Hal Leonard

Music arrangements Flamboyant, Miracles, Somewhere,
Where The Streets Have No Name by Pete Tomasso.
Music processed by Jon Bunker.

www.halleonard.com

Go West

Words & Music by Jacques Morali, Henri Belolo & Victor Willis

West, this___ is what we're gon - na do.___   gon - na do.___
West, this___ is our___ des - ti - ny.___   Go
West, this___ is what we're

C' - mon, c' - mon, c' - mon,___ c' - mon go West!

Go

West,   go West,   go

Suburbia

Words & Music by Neil Tennant & Chris Lowe

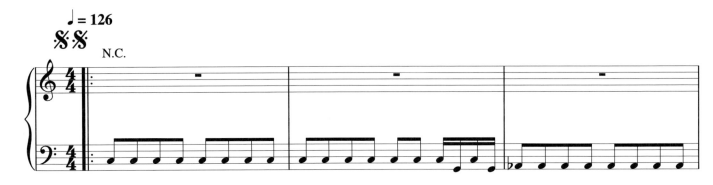

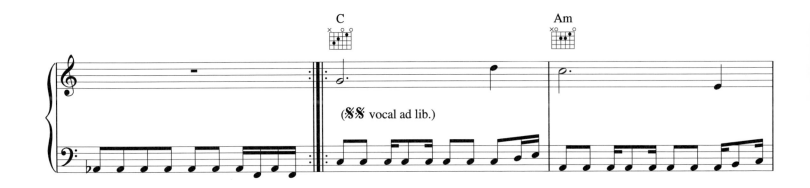

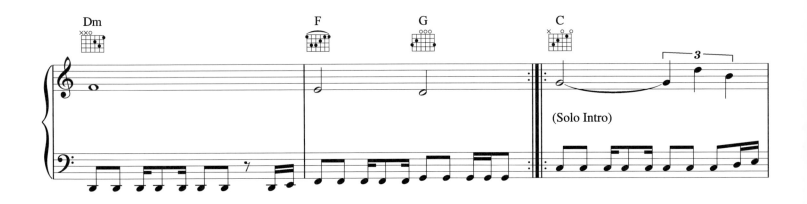

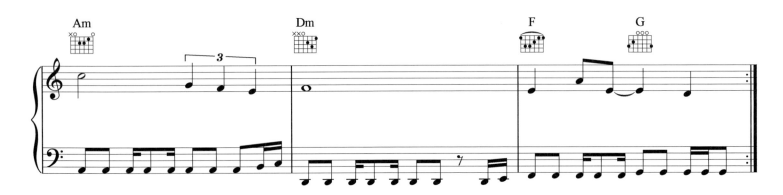

What have I done to deserve this?

Words & Music by Neil Tennant, Chris Lowe & Allee Willis

1. You al-ways want-ed a lov-er,   I on-ly want-ed a job.___
2. I come here look-ing for mon-ey (gotta have it)   and end up leav-ing with love.___
3. You al-ways want-ed me to be something I wasn't.   You al-ways want-ed too much.___

19

Se a vida é (That's the way life is)

Words by Neil Tennant
Music by Ademario, Wellington Epiderme Negra, Nego Do Barbalho, Neil Tennant & Chris Lowe

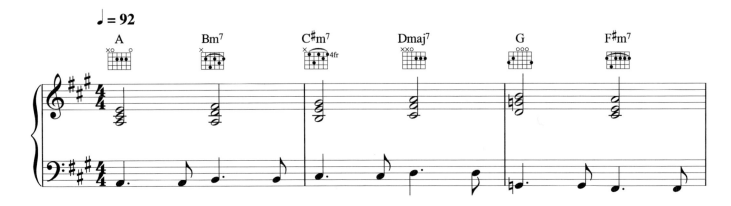

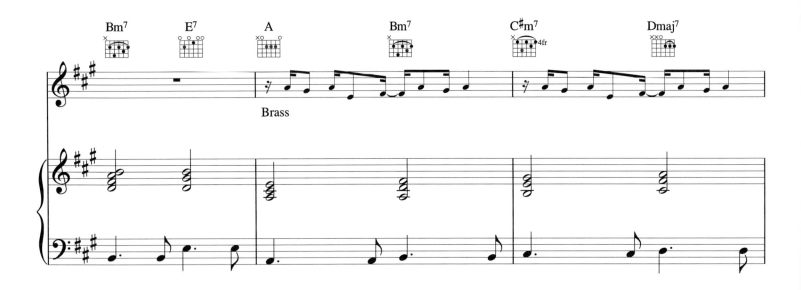

Brass

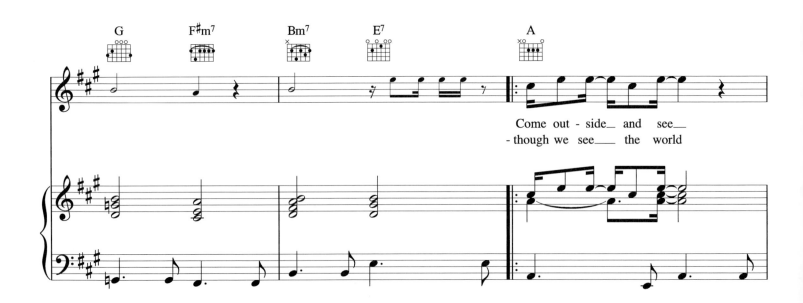

Come out - side___ and see___
- though we see___ the world

Always on my mind

Words & Music by Mark James, Wayne Thompson & Johnny Christopher

Lyrics:

May-be I did-n't treat you
May-be I did-n't hold you

quite as good as I should.
all those lone-ly, lone-ly times.

May-be I did-n't
And I guess I nev-er

Home and dry

Words & Music by Neil Tennant & Chris Lowe

Continues throughout

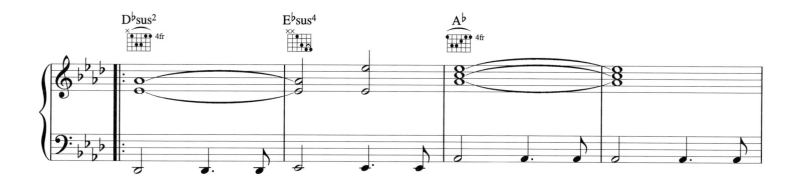

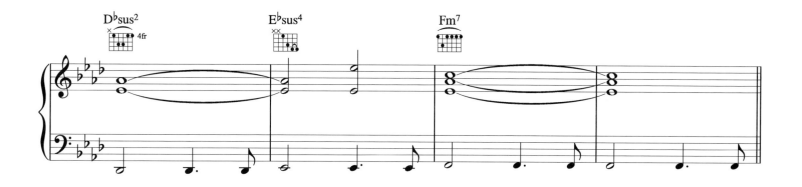

37

I wouldn't normally do this kind of thing

Words & Music by Neil Tennant & Chris Lowe

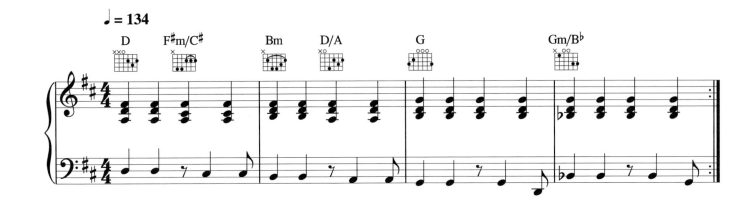

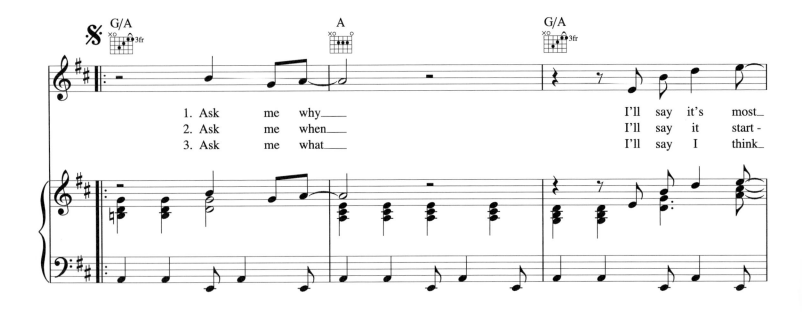

1. Ask me why___ I'll say it's most___
2. Ask me when___ I'll say it start-
3. Ask me what___ I'll say I think___

___ un-us-ual, how can I_____ e-ven try
-ed when I met you, and e-ver since then___ I knew that the past
___ it's good___ for you, be-lieve it or not___ I know where it's all___

Heart

Words & Music by Neil Tennant & Chris Lowe

44

3.
2nd verse only
Dm7 Em7 Am Dm7 Em7
oh ev - 'ry time.
ev - 'ry time.
Fmaj7 Em7 F#m7 F6
I hear your heart beat next to me
I'm in love
Am Dm7 Em7 Am
with you I mean what I say I'm in love with you and you don't
Dm7 Em7 Am G
To Coda
know what it means to be with you.
Beat

Miracles

Words & Music by Neil Tennant, Chris Lowe, Adam F & Dan Fresh Stein

where sun - light breaks through and sud - den - ly there's a blu - er sky__

__ when - ev - er you're a - round,_____ you al - ways

bring a blu - er sky,____ a bright - er day.____

51

fly_____ ev - en high - er in the sky,_____

sun shines_____ it's a new day,_____

it's a new__ day._____

Love comes quickly

Words & Music by Neil Tennant, Chris Lowe & Stephen Hague

3rd time only
(Sooner or later this happens to everyone)

(To everyone)

1. You can live

your life____ lone - ly____
life of lu - xu - ry____

hea - vy as____ stone____
if that's what you want

Domino dancing

Words & Music by Neil Tennant & Chris Lowe

It's a sin

Words & Music by Neil Tennant & Chris Lowe

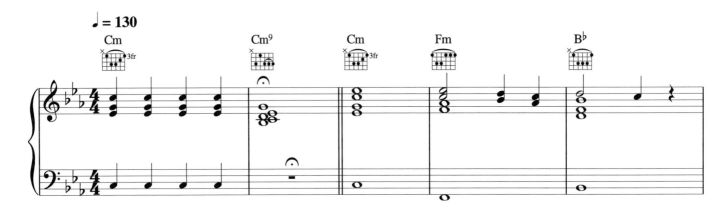

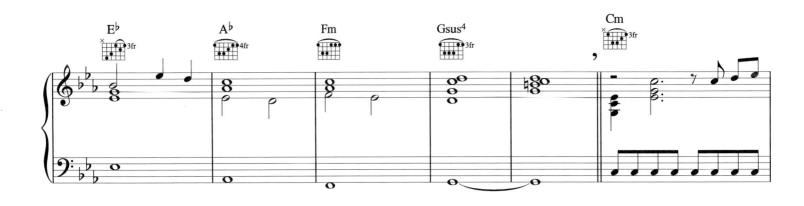

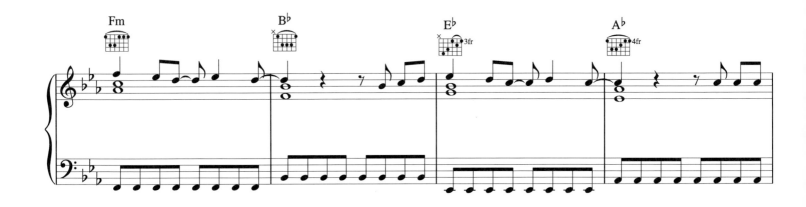

It's a,   it's a,   it's a,_____   it's a   sin.

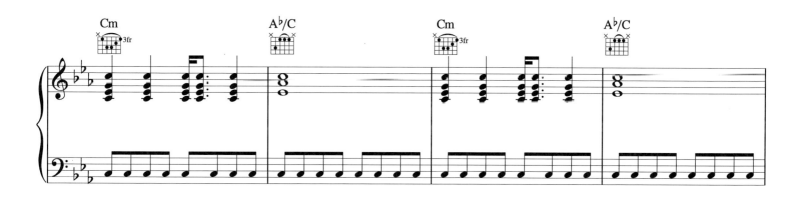

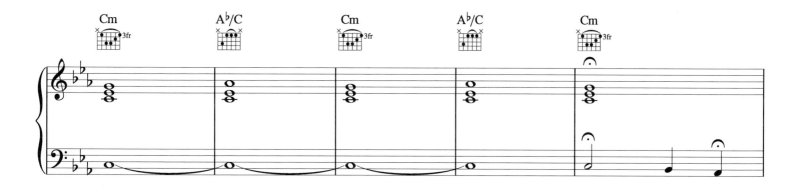

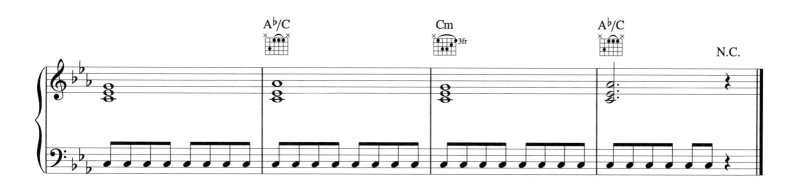

Before

Words & Music by Neil Tennant & Chris Lowe

The te - le - phone's__ not an - swered so ma - ny times__ you'll call,
So ma - ny fears__ will haunt__ you de - ny them or__ re - gret,
Co - in - ci - dence__ and pat - ience will mend this fa - tal flaw,

for ma - ny diff - 'rent rea - sons so ma - ny tears__ will fall.__ Be - fore
some men will make__ you want__ to and you will not__ for - get.__ Be - fore
though it may seem__ a long wait oth - ers have been__ here__ be - fore

you find_ your love,_ be- fore___ it comes knock-ing at__ your door,

be- fore__ you know_ for sure,__ this is what_ you were wait-ing for.

To Coda

1.

69

2.

Dm⁹   G   Am/E   Em

There's a sto-ry of a man who loved too much,__ he end-ed up__ in-side__ a pri-son cell.__

Dm⁹   G   Am/E   Em

__ You've got to want to give to get it, or you could land up in the same sus-pi-cious hell.__

F/A   Em⁷   Am/C

__ It's hap-pened be - fore,__

F/A   Em⁷   Am/C   *D. 𝄋 al Coda*

it's hap-pened be - fore.

Coda

One__ day when the phone starts ring-ing, you'll an-swer to the words you're long-ing for.__ No__ tears, no trade, no pri-son cell.__ What-ev-er you need we will re-turn more.__ It's hap-pened be-fore.__

repeat to fade

71

New York City boy

Words & Music by Neil Tennant, Chris Lowe & David Morales

74

you can re-
- turn its calls.

It's alright

Words & Music by Sterling Void & Paris Brightledge

80

Where the streets have no name
(I can't take my eyes off you)

Words & Music by U2

where the streets have no name, _____ can't take my

eyes off of you. _____

I love you ba - by and if it's

quite al - right I need you ba - by, to warm a

lone - ly night, so let me love you__ ba - by, let me

love you.___ 3. The ci - ties a - flood,

93

Flamboyant

Words & Music by Neil Tennant & Chris Lowe

1. You live in a world of ex - cess, where more is more, and less
2. You live in a time of de - cay, when the worth of a man is how much
3. There you are at an - other pre - view, in a pose the art -

____ is much less.____ A day with - out fame____ is a waste_ and a ques -
____ he can play.____ Ev -'ry day all the pub - lic must know_ where you are,
- ist and you.____ To look so loud, may be con - si - dered tack - y____ col - lect -

- tion of need is a ques - tion of taste.____ You're so____
____ what you do 'cause your life____ is a show, and you're so____
- ers wear black clothes by Is - sey Mi - ya - ke. You're so____

flam - bo - yant the way you live,___
flam - bo - yant the way you look,___

you real - ly care___ that they stare___ and the press___
it gets you so___ much at - ten - tion, your sole___

de - ploy - ment is al - ways there,___
em - ploy - ment is get - ting more,___

To Coda ⊕

it's what you do___ for en - joy - ment.
you want po - lice___ in - ter - ven - tion.

1.

It all takes cour - age you know it, just cross - ing the street, well it's al - most he - ro - ic you're so flam - bo - yant.

D.S. al Coda

102

A red letter day

Words & Music by Neil Tennant & Chris Lowe

Left to my own devices

Words & Music by Neil Tennant & Chris Lowe

get out of bed at half past ten and
2. Pick up a bro - chure a - bout the sun.
3. when you look the way you do, the

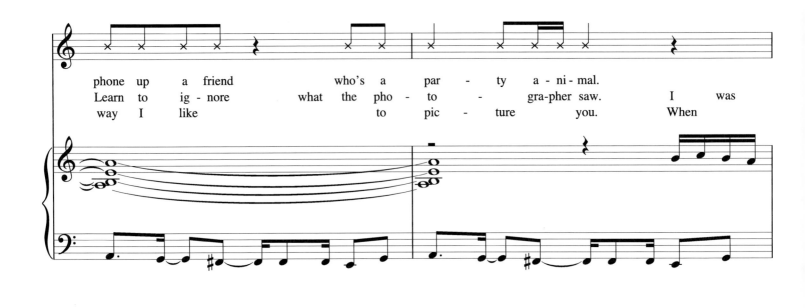

phone up a friend who's a par - ty a - ni - mal.
Learn to ig - nore what the pho - to - gra-pher saw. I was
way I like to pic - ture you. When

Dm

Turn on the news and drink some tea;___ may - be if
al - ways told that you should join a club;___
I get home it's late at night,___ I

you're with me we'll do some shop - ping.
stick with the gang if you want to be - long. I was a
pour a drink and watch the fight

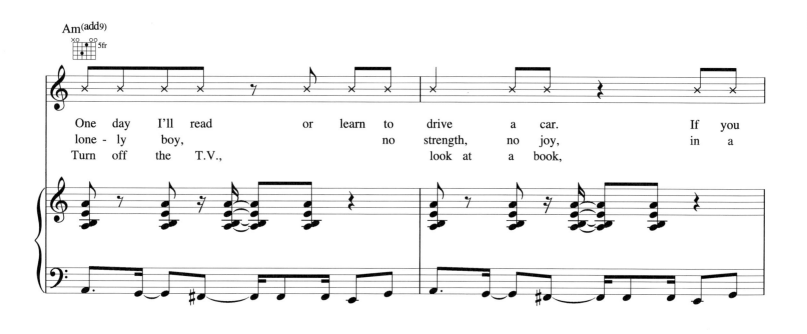

One day I'll read or learn to drive a car. If you
lone - ly boy, no strength, no joy,
Turn off the T.V., look at a book,

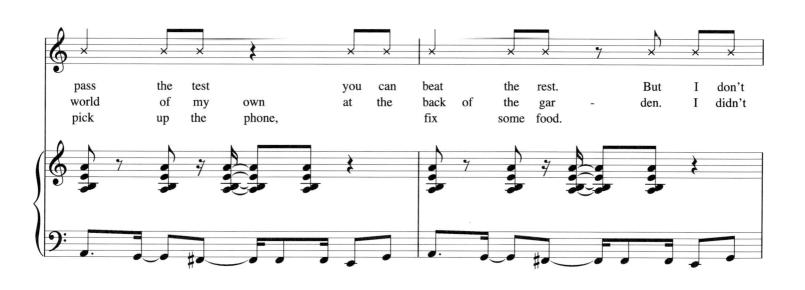

pass the test you can beat the rest. But I don't
world of my own at the back of the gar - den. I didn't
pick up the phone, fix some food.

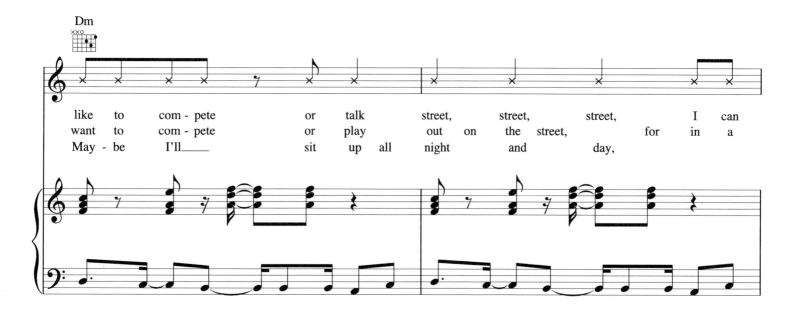

like to com - pete or talk street, street, street, I can
want to com - pete or play out on the street, for in a
May - be I'll___ sit up all night and day,

115

119

I don't know what you want
but I can't give it anymore

Words & Music by Neil Tennant & Chris Lowe

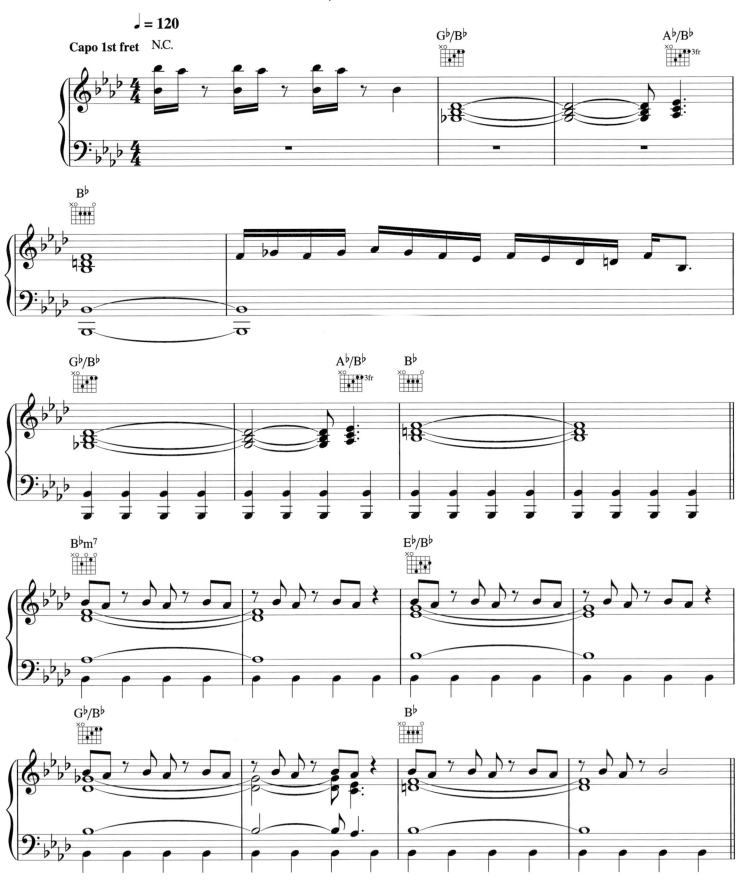

1. Did you get what you want?___ Do you know what it is?___ Do you
2. Was it crack-ing the code___ or just fill-ing in time?___ Was that

care?___ Is he bet-ter than me?___ Was it your place___ or
all?___ So then why'd you go back___ to the scene of___ the

his? Who was there?___ Did you think it was wrong?___
crime? Did he call?___ Shall I take fur-ther blame___

___ Do you find that it's worse than it was?___ Has it gone on too long?___
___ or a-no-ther as-sault on how it was?___ Then we'll get to the fact___

121

don't know what you want, but I can't give it a-ny-more.___ I

don't know what you want, but I can't give it a-ny-more.___

1. You're_____ break- ing__ my__ heart.___

2. Don't know what__ you want.

123

Don't know what__ you want.

don't know what you want, but I can't give it a - ny - more.__

don't know what you want, but I can't give it a - ny - more.___

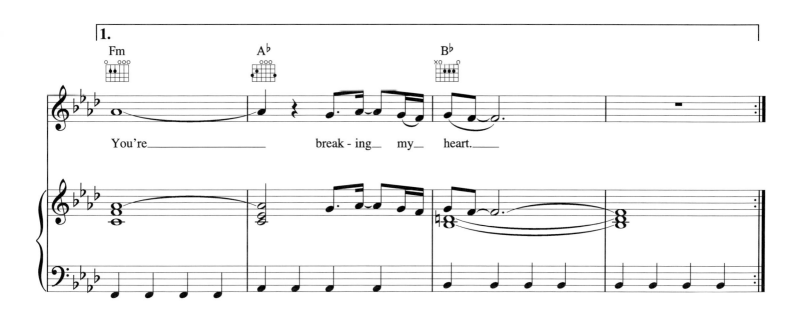

1.

You're_____ break - ing___ my___ heart.___

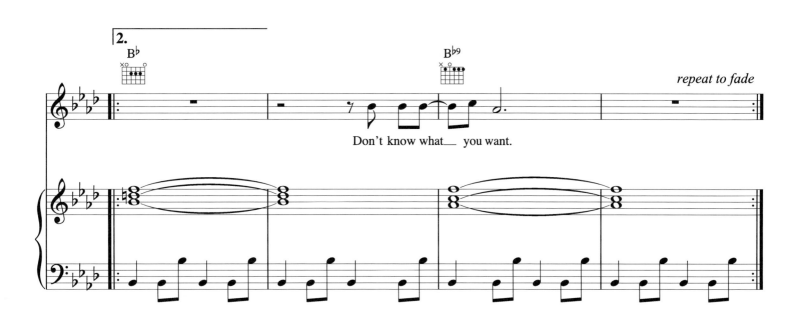

2.

repeat to fade

Don't know what___ you want.

Being boring

Words & Music by Neil Tennant & Chris Lowe

Can you forgive her?

Words & Music by Neil Tennant & Chris Lowe

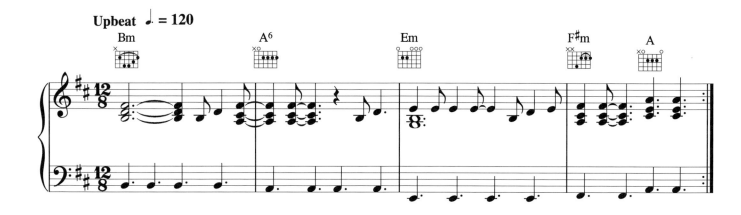

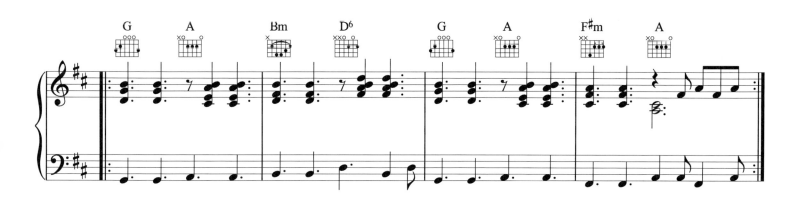

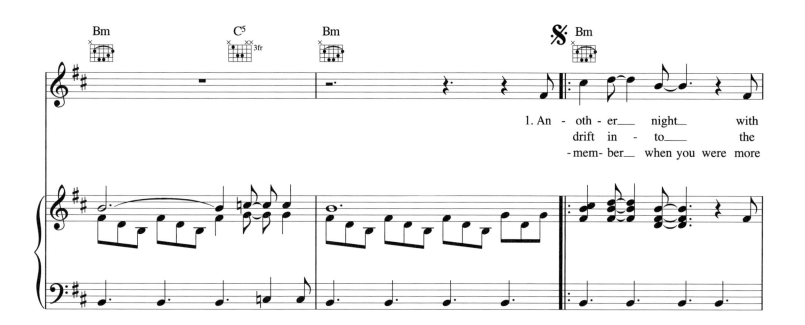

1. An - oth - er night with
drift in - to the
- mem - ber when you were more

o-pen eyes,___ too late to___ sleep,___ too soon to___ rise.___ You're
stran - gest___ dreams___ of youth - ful fol - lies and chang - ing___ teams.___ Ad-
ea - si - ly lead___ behind the cric - ket pa - vi - lion and the bi - cy - cle shed.___

short of___ breath,___ is it a heart at - tack?___ Hot and___ fev - er - ish, you
-mit you're wrong – Oh, no! Not___ yet! – Then you wake up and re-mem - ber that you
Trem - bling___ as___ your dreams came___ true, you looked right___ in - to those blue

face the___ fact, you're in love___ and it feels___ like___ shame___ be-cause she's
can't for - get. She's made you___ somekind of laugh - ing___ stock___ be-cause you
eyes and___ knew, it was love___ and now you can't pre - tend___ you've for-

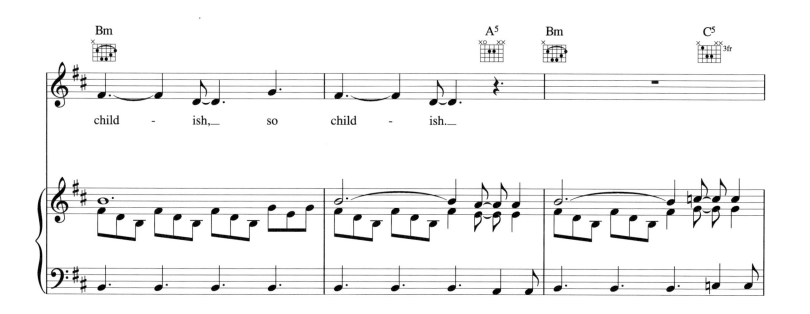

D. %. al Coda

$\oplus$ *Coda*

West End girls

Words & Music by Neil Tennant & Chris Lowe

So hard

Words & Music by Neil Tennant & Chris Lowe

I get along

Words & Music by Neil Tennant & Chris Lowe

1. Feel - ing like I'm stuck in a hole,__
2. Now I know you'd much rath - er be__

Rent

Words & Music by Neil Tennant & Chris Lowe

You dress me up   I'm your pup - pet   you buy me things

D. % al Coda

I love it

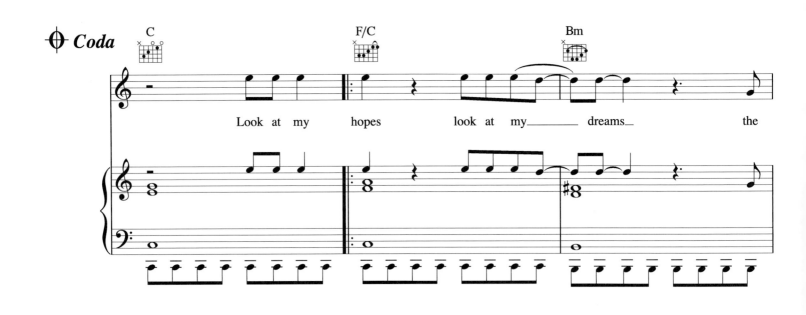

Look at my hopes   look at my____ dreams____   the

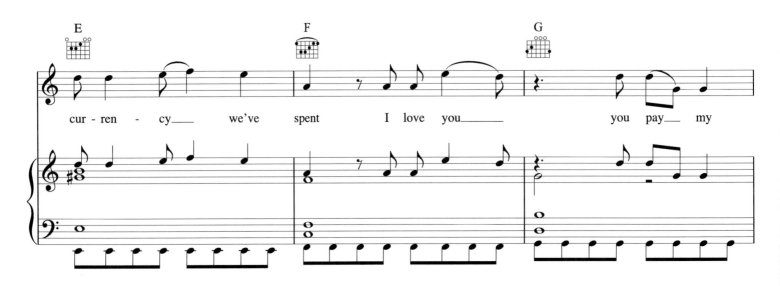

cur - ren - cy____   we've spent   I love you____   you pay__ my

Jealousy

Words & Music by Neil Tennant & Chris Lowe

1. At dead of night,___ when___ stran - gers roam___
2. I lie a - lone,___ the___ clock strikes three,___
(3.) - y I ne - ver knew___ time___ pass so slow,___

the streets in search___ of___ a - ny - one___ who'll
and a - ny - one___ who___ want - ed to___ could
I wish I'd ne - ver___ met you, or___ that

take them home.
con - tact me.
I could bear to   let you   go. ___

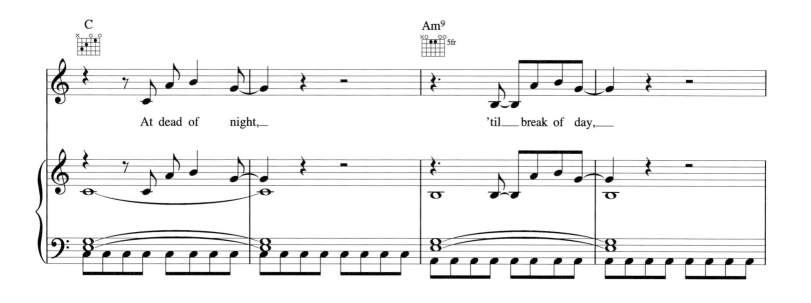

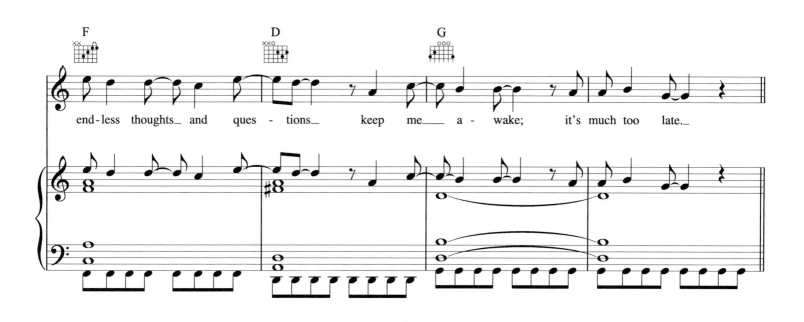

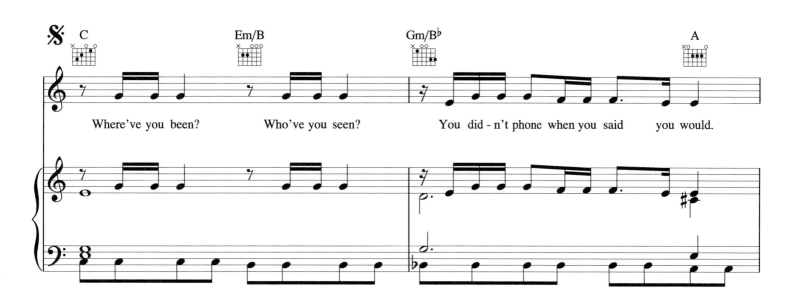

Do you lie? Do you try to keep in touch? You know you could. I've

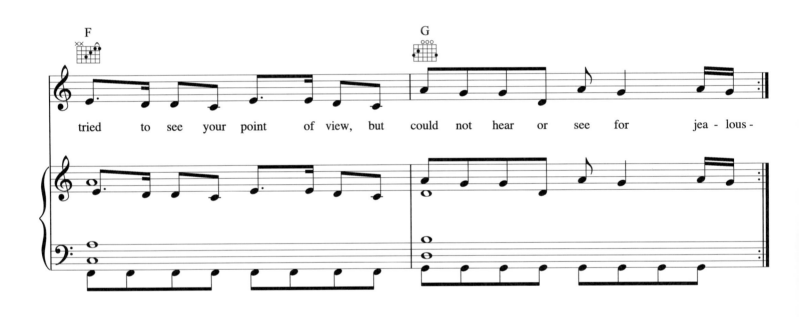

tried to see your point of view, but could not hear or see for jea - lous -

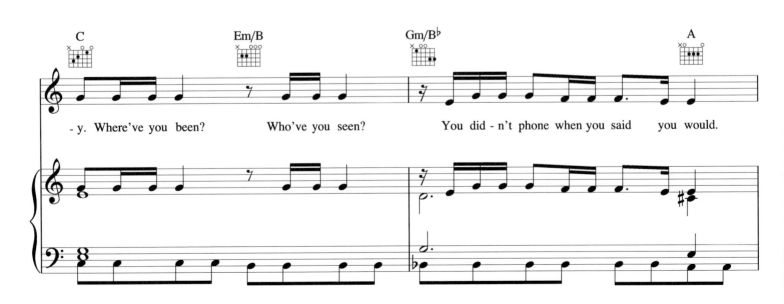

- y. Where've you been? Who've you seen? You did - n't phone when you said you would.

D. 𝄋 al Coda

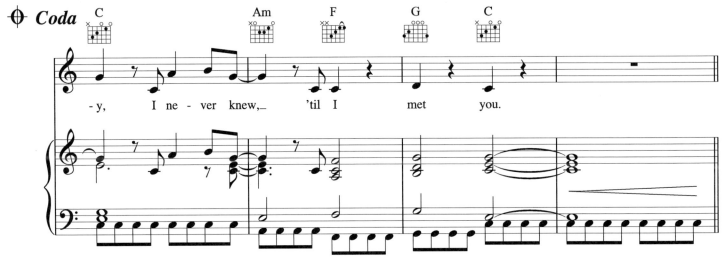

-y, I ne - ver knew,___ 'til I met you.

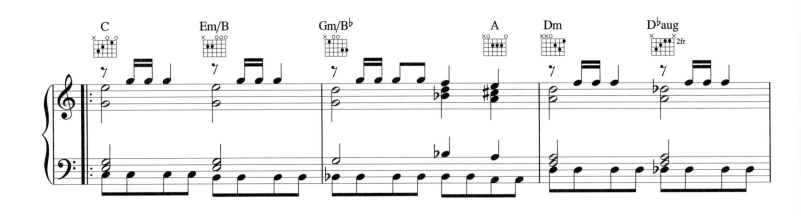

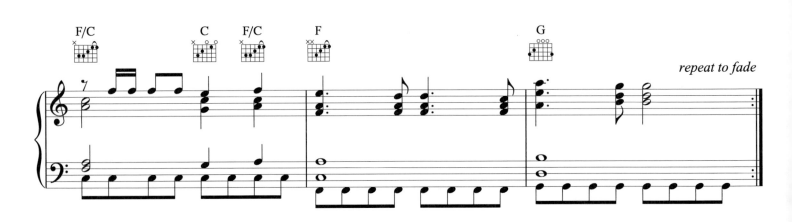

repeat to fade

160

Liberation

Words & Music by Neil Tennant & Chris Lowe

Lyrics: 1. Take my hand,___ I've_ changed___ my_____ mind a - gain.

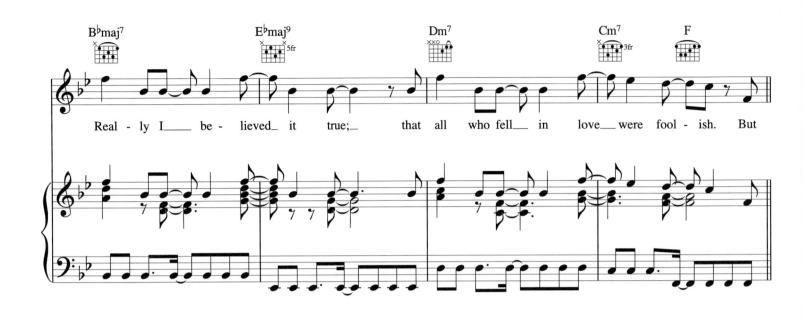

Real - ly I ___ be - lieved_ it true;__ that all who fell__ in love__ were fool - ish. But

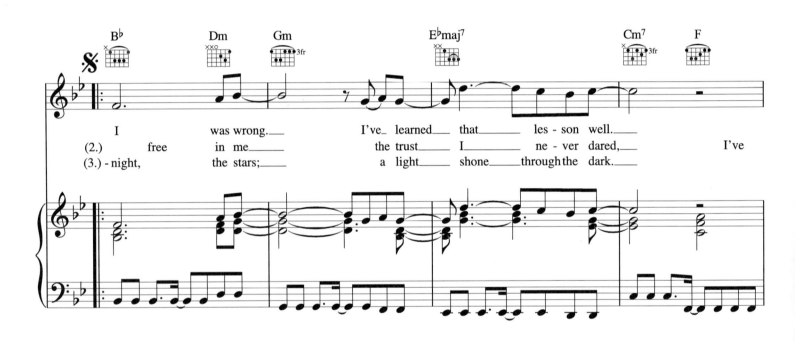

I ___ was wrong.___ I've_ learned__ that____ les - son well.___

(2.) ___ free in me____ the trust___ I ___ ne - ver dared,___ I've

(3.) - night, the stars;___ a light__ shone__through the dark.__

All the way__ back home__ at mid - night, you were sleep - ing on_

al - ways thought the risk__ too_ great,___ but sud - den - ly__ I don't

All the way__ back home__ at mid - night, you were sleep - ing on__

164

DJ culture

Words & Music by Neil Tennant & Chris Lowe

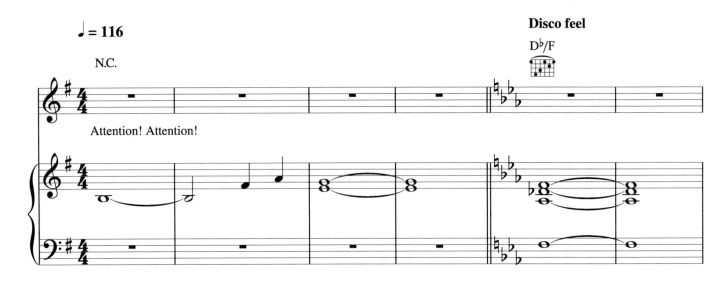

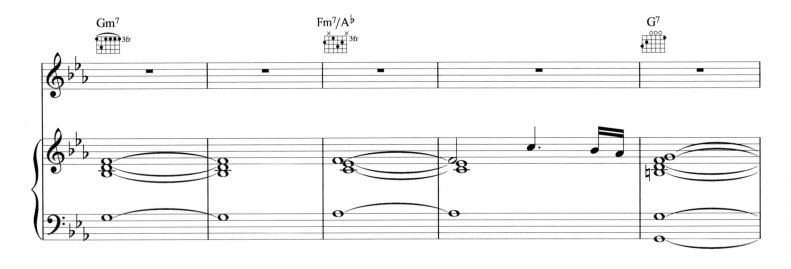

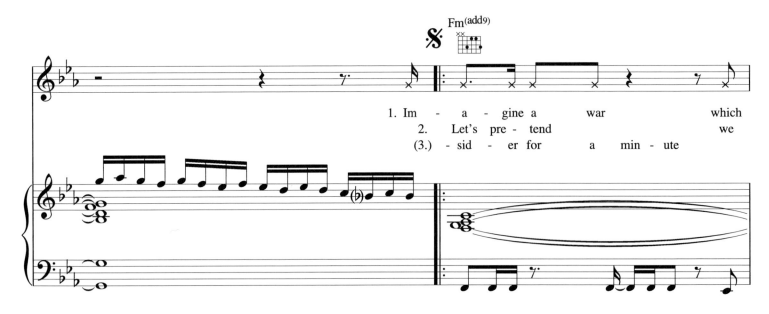

po - si - tive or frank - ly   re - al - is - tic.
seen it all,_____ the change of sea - sons.
sud-den-ly you're miss-ing, then you're re - born.

Which is   ter - rib - ly old fa - shioned,
And   I,   my   lord,
And   I,   my   lord,

is - n't it?   Or is - n't it?
may I_____   say   no - thing?
may I_____   say   no - thing?

(D.   J.   Cul - ture)

Dance   with me,___   (D. J. Cul - ture)   let's   pre - tend,___

fan - ta-sy___ won-der - ing who's___ your friend.___

(D. J. Cul-ture)

Now___ as a mat-ter of pride

in - dulge your-self,___ your ev - 'ry

mood,___ no feast-days or fast-days or

You only tell me you love me when you're drunk

Words & Music by Neil Tennant & Chris Lowe

You on - ly tell___ me you love me when you're drunk.___

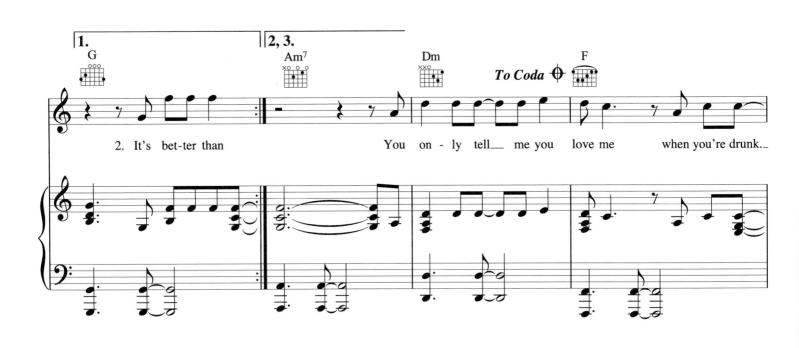

1. G

2, 3. Am⁷   Dm   *To Coda* ⊕ F

2. It's bet-ter than

You on - ly tell___ me you love me when you're drunk.___

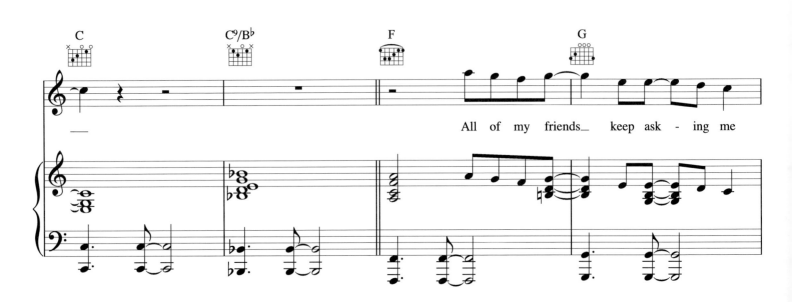

C   C⁹/B♭   F   G

___   All of my friends___ keep ask - ing me

Opportunities
(Let's make lots of money)

Words & Music by Neil Tennant & Chris Lowe

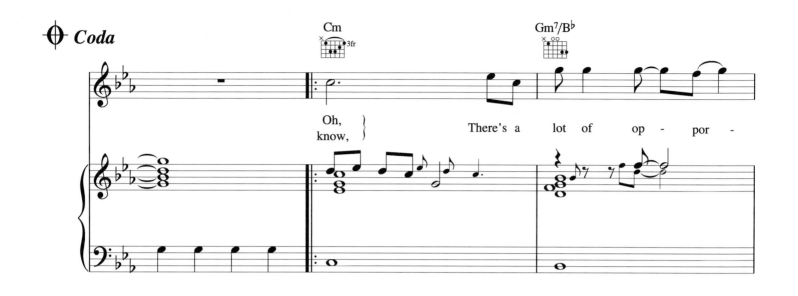

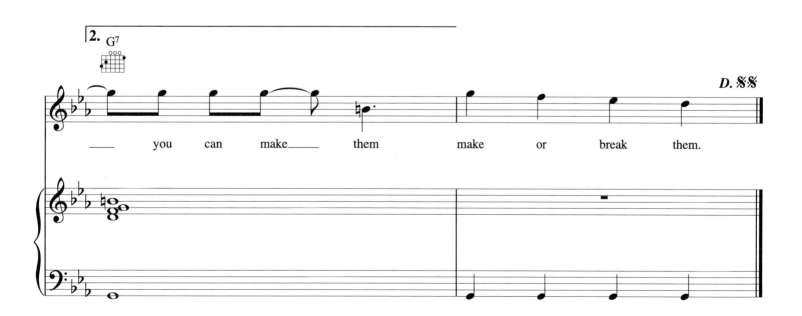

179

Yesterday, when I was mad

Words & Music by Neil Tennant & Chris Lowe

1. 'Dar - ling, you were won - der - ful,___ you
2. have a cer - tain qua - li - ty which

really were quite good, / really is unique;   I enjoyed it, though of course / expressionless, such irony,   no-one understood / although your voice is weak.   a / It

word of what was going on. They / doesn't really matter 'cause the / 3. Then we posed for pictures with the   didn't have a clue. / music is so loud, / competition winners and   They / of

couldn't understand your sense of / course it's all on tape / argued 'bout the hotel rooms and   humour like I do.' / but no-one-'ll find out.' / where to go for dinner.   'You're / You / And

much too kind,' / hated me too / someone said: 'It's fabulous you're still around today.   I smiled, / but not as /   with / much as / You've

A♭   A♭/E♭

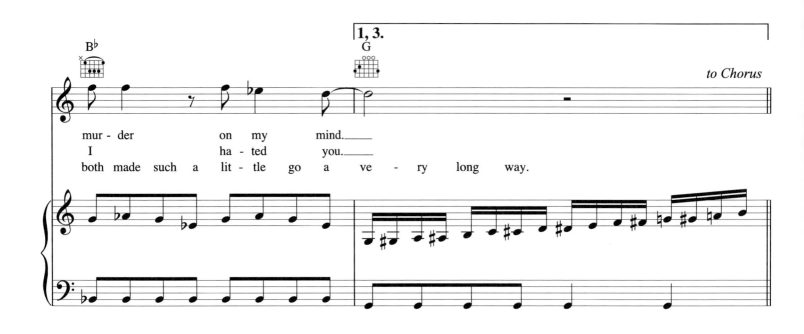

mur - der   on my   mind.____
I   ha - ted   you.____
both made such a lit - tle go a ve - ry long way.

Chorus

Yes - ter - day,__   when I___ was mad__   and

Paninaro '95

Words & Music by Neil Tennant & Chris Lowe

189

190

193

194

Single-Bilingual

Words & Music by Neil Tennant & Chris Lowe

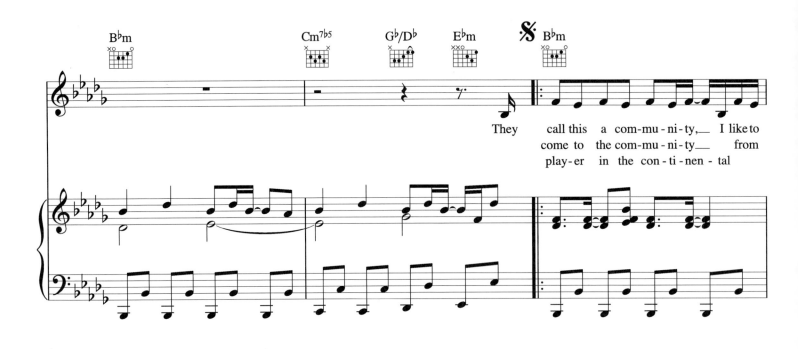

They   call this   a com-mu - ni-ty,___ I like to
come to   the com-mu - ni-ty___   from
play-er   in the con - ti -nen - tal

think of   it   as   home.___   Ar - riv - ing   at   the   air - port,   I   am
U. K.   p. l.   c.,___   ar - riv - ing   at   my   ho - tel,   there   are
game,   with   un - li - mi - ted   ex - pens - es   to   re -

go - ing   it   a - lone.___   Or - der - ing   a   board - ing   pass,   tra - vel - ling   in___
fax - es   greet - ing   me.___   Stay - ing   in   a   ju - nior   suite   so there's room   to___
- claim.   In - for - ma-tion's   ea - sy;   tap - ping   at   my___

sin - gle,__ bi - lin - gual,__ sin - gle,__ bi - lin - gual.__

Hay u - na dis - co - te - ca por__ ac - qui? Hay u - na dis - co te__ ca por__ ac - qui?

Hay u - na dis - co - te - ca por__ ac - qui? Hay u - na dis - co te__ ca por__ ac - qui?

repeat twice

199

Somewhere

Words by Stephen Sondheim
Music by Leonard Bernstein

some - how,_____ some - day,_____

some - where._____